Robber
Rabbit

Robber Rabbit

by **Alice Hemming**
illustrated by **Serena Lombardo**

'Robber Rabbit'
An original concept by Alice Hemming
© Alice Hemming

Illustrated by Serena Lombardo

Published by MAVERICK ARTS PUBLISHING LTD
Studio 3A, City Business Centre, 6 Brighton Road,
Horsham, West Sussex, RH13 5BB
© Maverick Arts Publishing Limited August 2018
+44 (0)1403 256941

A CIP catalogue record for this book is available at the British Library.

ISBN 978-1-84886-366-8

www.maverickbooks.co.uk

Yellow

This book is rated as: Yellow Band (Guided Reading)
This story is decodable at Letters and Sounds Phase 3/4.

Jaz is a rabbit.

He hops, eats and naps.

Jaz digs under the road
and pops up in a garden.

Jaz sniffs. He can smell good things!

Carrot chips,

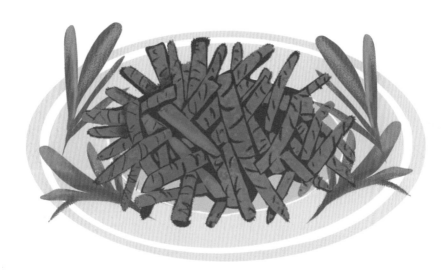

carrot salad,

and carrot tops!

Jaz puts the food in his sack.

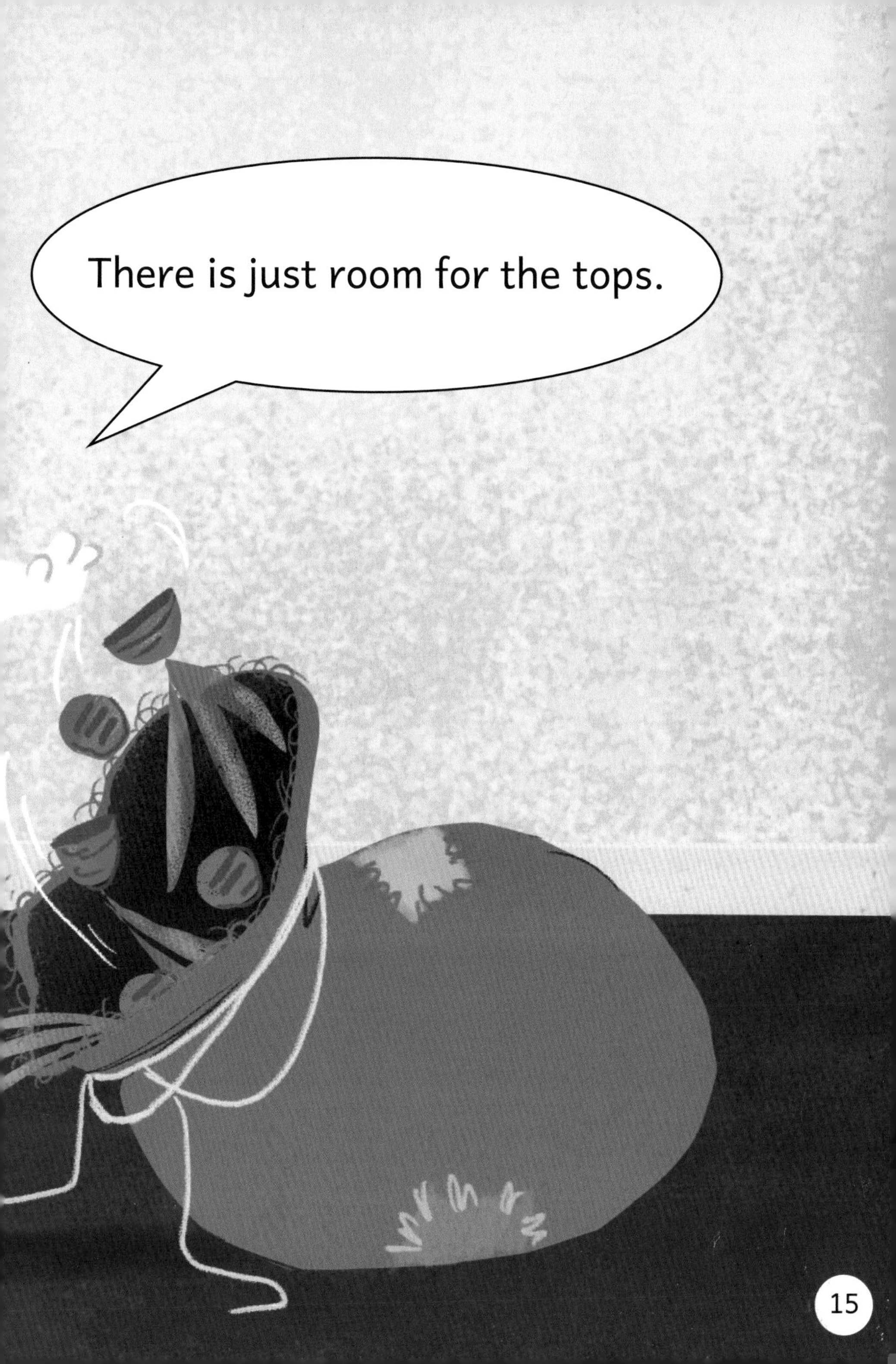
There is just room for the tops.

Jaz hears feet. It is a man.

A big, cross man.

I had better hop off!

But Jaz cannot pick up the sack.

Whee!

Jaz gets rid of the salad.

The sack is too full.

Whee! Jaz gets rid of the chips.

Hop, hop!

Jaz needs to get the sack in the tunnel.

Whee! Jaz gets rid of the carrot tops.

Jaz gets back.

Quiz

1. What is Jaz?
a) A King Rabbit
b) A Robber Rabbit
c) A Pirate Rabbit

2. What does Jaz want to eat?
a) Potatoes
b) Tomatoes
c) Carrots

3. Where does Jaz find carrots?
a) In a kitchen
b) In a shed
c) Underground

4. Why can't Jaz run away?

a) The sack is too full

b) He falls asleep

c) He eats too much

5. What does Jaz get in his sack?

a) Lots and lots

b) Not much

c) Nothing

Turn over for answers

Book Bands for Guided Reading

Pink
Red
Yellow
Blue
Green
Orange
Turquoise
Purple
Gold
White

The Institute of Education book banding system is a scale of colours that reflects the various levels of reading difficulty. The bands are assigned by taking into account the content, the language style, the layout and phonics.

Maverick Early Readers are a bright, attractive range of books covering the pink to purple bands. All of these books have been book banded for guided reading to the industry standard and edited by a leading educational consultant.

To view the whole Maverick Readers scheme, visit our website at

www.maverickearlyreaders.com

Or scan the QR code above to view our scheme instantly!

Quiz Answers: 1b, 2c, 3a, 4a, 5b